KU-157-876

# Sing With Me this Christmas

Illustrations & design by
**Isabelle Charbonneau**
with the collaboration of Annie Cossette & Péo

## 25 most beautiful Christmas Songs

# Up On The Housetop

Up on the housetop, reindeer pause
Out jumps good ol' Santa Claus
Down through the chimney with lots of toys
All for the little ones, Christmas joys
Ho, Ho, Ho! Who wouldn't go?
Ho, Ho, Ho! Who wouldn't go?
Up on the housetop, click, click, click
Down through the chimney with good Saint Nick.

First comes the stocking of little Nell
Oh, dear Santa, fill it well
Give her a dolly that laughs and cries
One that will open and shut her eyes
Ho, Ho, Ho! Who wouldn't go?
Ho, Ho, Ho! Who wouldn't go?
Up on the housetop, click, click, click
Down through the chimney with good Saint Nick.

Next comes the stocking of little Will
Oh, just see what a glorious fill
Here is a hammer and lots of tacks
Also a ball and a whip that cracks
Ho, Ho, Ho! Who wouldn't go?
Ho, Ho, Ho! Who wouldn't go?
Up on the housetop, click, click, click
Down through the chimney with good Saint Nick.

# Do You Hear What I Hear?

Said the night wind to the little lamb
Do you see what I see, do you see what I see?
Way up in the sky little lamb
Do you see what I see, do you see what I see?
A star, a star
Dancing in the night
With a tail as big as a kite
With a tail as big as a kite

Said the little lamb to the shepherd boy
Do you hear what I hear, do you hear what I hear?
Ringing through the sky shepherd boy
Do you hear what I hear, do you hear what I hear?
A song, a song
High above the tree
With a voice as big as the sea
With a voice as big as the sea

Said the shepherd boy to the mighty King
Do you know what I know, do you know what I know?
In your palace wall mighty King
Do you know what I know, do you know what I know?
A child, a child
Shivers in the cold
Let us bring him silver and gold
Let us bring him silver and gold

Said the King to the people everywhere
Listen to what I say, listen to what I say?
Pray for peace people everywhere
Listen to what I say
The child, the child
Sleeping in the night
He will bring us goodness and light
He will bring us goodness and light

# Rudolph, the Red-Nosed Reindeer

You know Dasher and Dancer
and Prancer and Vixen,
Comet and Cupid and
Donner and Blitzen,
But do you recall?
The most famous reindeer of all?

Rudolph the Red-Nosed Reindeer
Had a very shiny nose,
And if you ever saw him,
You would even say it glows.
All of the other reindeer
Used to laugh and call him names;
They never let poor Rudolph
Join in any reindeer games.

Then one foggy Christmas Eve,
Santa came to say,
"Rudolph, with your nose so bright,
Won't you lead my sleigh tonight?"
Then all the reindeer loved him
As they shouted out with glee:
Rudolph the Red-Nosed Reindeer,
you'll go down in history.

Rudolph the Red-Nosed Reindeer
Had a very shiny nose,
And if you ever saw him,

You would even say it glows.
All of the other reindeer
Used to laugh and call him names;
They never let poor Rudolph
Join in any reindeer games.

Then one foggy Christmas Eve,
Santa came to say,
"Rudolph with your nose so bright,
Won't you lead my sleigh tonight?"
Then all the reindeer loved him
As they shouted out with glee:
Rudolph, the Red-Nosed Reindeer,
you'll go down in history.

# Joy to the World

Traditional

Joy to the world! The Lord has come;
Let earth receive her King!
Let every heart prepare Him room
And heaven and nature sing
And heaven and nature sing
And heaven and heaven and nature sing

Joy to the earth! The Savior reigns;
Let men their songs employ
While fields and floods rocks, hills, and plains
Repeat the sounding joy
Repeat the sounding joy
Repeat, repeat the sounding joy

No more let sins and sorrows grow
Nor thorns infest my ground:
He comes to make his blessing flow
Far as the curse is found
Far as the curse is found
Far as, far as the curse is found

He rules the world with truth and grace
And makes the nations prove
The glories of His righteousness
And wonders of His love
And wonders of His love
And wonders, wonders of His love

Dashing through the snow
In a one horse-open sleigh
O'er the fields we go
Laughing all the way
Bells on bob-tail ring
Making spirits bright
What fun it is to ride and sing
A sleighing song tonight

Oh, jingle bells, jingle bells
Jingle all the way
Oh, what fun it is to ride
In a one horse-open sleigh
Jingle bells, jingle bells,
Jingle all the way
Oh, what fun it is to ride
In a one horse-open sleigh

Dashing through the snow
In a one horse-open sleigh
O'er the fields we go
Laughing all the way
Bells on bob-tail ring
Making spirits bright
What fun it is to ride and sing
A sleighing song tonight

Oh jingle bells, jingle bells
Jingle all the way
Oh what fun it is to ride
In a one horse-open sleigh
Jingle bells, jingle bells,
Jingle all the way
Oh, what fun it is to ride
In a one horse-open sleigh

10

# Silent Night

Traditional

Silent night, holy night
All is calm, all is bright
Round yon Virgin Mother and Child
Holy Infant so tender and mild
Sleep in heavenly peace
Sleep in heavenly peace

Silent night, holy night!
Shepherds quake at the sight
Glories stream from heaven afar
Heavenly hosts sing Alleluia!
Christ, the Saviour is born
Christ, the Saviour is born

Chorus

Sleep in heavenly peace
Sleep in heavenly peace
Christ, the Saviour is born

# Santa Claus Is Comin' to Town

You better watch out
You better not cry
You better not pout
I'm telling you why
Santa Claus is coming to town

He's making a list,
And checking it twice;
Gonna find out who's naughty or nice.
Santa Claus is coming to town

He sees you when you're sleeping
He knows when you're awake
He knows if you've been bad or good
So be good for goodness sake

Oh you better watch out
You better not cry
You better not pout
I'm telling you why
Santa Claus is coming to town

You better watch out
You better not cry
You better not pout
I'm telling you why
Santa Claus is coming to town

He's making a list,
And checking it twice;
Gonna find out who's naughty or nice.
Santa Claus is coming to town

He sees you when you're sleeping
He knows when you're awake
He knows if you've been bad or good
So be good for goodness sake

Oh you better watch out
You better not cry
You better not pout
I'm telling you why
Santa Claus is coming to town

# The Little Drummer Boy

Come, they told him, pa rum pum pum pum
A newborn King to see, pa rum pum pum pum
Our finest gifts we bring, pa rum pum pum pum
To lay before the King, pa rum pum pum pum,
Rum pum pum pum, rum pum pum pum
So to honor Him, pa rum pum pum pum
When we come

Baby Jesus, pa rum pum pum pum
I am a poor boy too, pa rum pum pum pum
I have no gift to bring, pa rum pum pum pum
That's fit to give our King, pa rum pum pum pum
Rum pum pum pum, rum pum pum pum
Shall I play for You? pa rum pum pum pum
On my drum

Mary nodded, pa rum pum pum pum
The ox and lamb kept time, pa rum pum pum pum
I played my drum for Him, pa rum pum pum pum
He played his best for Him, pa rum pum pum pum
Rum pum pum pum, rum pum pum pum
Then He smiled at me, pa rum pum pum pum
Me and my drum........

# Frosty the Snowman

Frosty the snowman was a jolly,  happy soul
With a corncob pipe and a button nose
and two eyes made out of coal
Frosty the snowman is a fairy tale they say
He was made of snow but the children
know how he came to life one day
There must have been some magic in that
old silk hat they found
For when they placed it on his head
he began to dance around

Frosty the snowman, was alive as he could be;
And the children say he could laugh and play,
 just the same as you and me.

Frosty the snowman knew
the sun was hot that day,
So he said,
"Let's run and
we'll have some fun
now before I melt away."
 Down to the village,
with a broomstick in his hand,
Running here and there, all
around the square, saying
"Catch me if you can!"

He led them down the streets of town
right to the traffic cop;
And he only paused a moment, when
he heard him holler "Stop!"
Frosty the snowman
had to hurry on his way
But he waved goodbye sayin
"Don't you cry,
I'll be back again some day!"

# The first Noel

Traditional

The first Noel the angels did say
Was to certain poor shepherds in fields as they lay
In fields where they lay, keeping their sheep
On a cold winter's night that was so deep

(Chorus)
Noel, Noel, Noel, Noel,
Born is the King of Israel!

They looked up and saw a star
Shining in the East beyond them far,
And to the earth it gave great light,
And so it continued both day and night.

(Chorus)

And by the light of that same star
Three Wise men came from country far;
To seek for a King was their intent,
And to follow the star wherever it went.

(Chorus)

This star drew nigh to the northwest,
O'er Bethlehem it took it rest,
And there it did both stop and stay
Right o'er the place where Jesus lay.

(Chorus)

Then let us all with one accord
Sing praises to our heavenly Lord;
That hath made Heaven and earth of nought,
And with his blood mankind hath bought.

(Chorus)

# Deck The Halls

Traditional

Deck the halls with boughs of holly
Fa, la, la, la, la, la, la, la, la
'Tis the season to be jolly
Fa, la, la, la, la, la, la, la, la
Don we now our gay apparel
Fa, la, la, la, la, la, la, la, la
Troll the ancient Yuletide carol
Fa, la, la, la, la, la, la, la, la

See the blazing yule before us
Fa, la, la, la, la, la, la, la, la
Strike the harp and join the chorus
Fa, la, la, la, la, la, la, la, la
Follow me in merry measure
Fa, la, la, la, la, la, la, la, la
While I tell of Yuletide treasure
Fa, la, la, la, la, la, la, la, la

# We Wish You a Merry Christmas

Traditional

We wish you a Merry Christmas;
We wish you a Merry Christmas;
We wish you a Merry Christmas and a Happy New Year

Good tidings to you were ever you are;
Good tidings for Christmas and a happy New Year

Please bring us a figgy pudding;
Please bring us a figgy pudding;
Please bring us a figgy pudding and a cup of good cheer

Good tidings to you were ever you are;
Good tidings for Christmas and a happy new Year

We won't go until we get some;
We won't go until we get some;
We won't go until we get some please bring some out here

We wish you a Merry Christmas;
We wish you a Merry Christmas;
We wish you a Merry Christmas and a Happy New Year

# Jolly Old Saint Nicholas

Jolly ol' Saint Nicholas,
lean your ear this way!
Don't you tell a single soul
what I'm going to say:
Christmas Eve is coming soon;
now, you dear old man
Whisper what you'll bring to me:
tell me if you can.

When the clock is striking twelve,
when I'm fast asleep
Down the chimney, broad and black,
with your pack you'll creep
All the stockings you will find
hanging in a row
Mine will be the shortest one,
you'll be sure to know

Bobby wants a pair of skates,
Suzy wants a sled
Nellie wants a picture book,
yellow, blue, and red
Now I think I'll leave to you
what to give the rest
Choose for me, dear Santa Claus;
you will know the best.

# Winter Wonderland

Sleigh bells ring
are you listening
in the lanes
snow is glistening
A beautiful sight
we're happy tonight
walking in a winter wonderland

Gone away is the bluebird
here to stay is the new bird
He sings a love song
as we go along
walking in a winter wonderland

In the meadow we can build a snowman
Then pretend that he is Parson Brown
He'll say: Are you married?
we'll say: No man
You can do the job
when you're in town

Later on
we'll conspire
as we dream by the fire
To face unafraid
the plans that we've made
walking in a winter wonderland

In the meadow we can build a snowman
and pretend that he's a circus clown
We'll have lots of fun with mister snowman
until the other kids knock him down

When it snows
ain't it thrilling
Though your nose gets a chilling
We'll frolic and play
the Eskimo way
walking in a winter wonderland

We'll sing a love song
as we go along
walking in a winter wonderland

# Let It Snow!

Oh the weather outside is frightful
But the fire is so delightful
And since we've no place to go
Let It Snow! Let It Snow! Let It Snow!

It doesn't show signs of stopping
And I've brought some corn for popping
The lights are turned way down low
Let It Snow! Let It Snow! Let It Snow!

When we finally say goodnight
How I'll hate going out in the storm!
But if you'll really hold me tight
All the way home I'll be warm

The fire is slowly dying
And, my dear, we're still good-bying
But as long as you love me so
Let It Snow! Let It Snow! Let It Snow!
Let It Snow! Let It Snow! Let It Snow!
Let It Snow! Let It Snow! Let It Snow!

When we finally say goodnight
How I'll hate going out in the storm!
But if you'll really hold me tight
All the way home I'll be warm

The fire is slowly dying
And, my dear, we're still good-bying
But as long as you love me so
Let It Snow! Let It Snow! Let It Snow!

# What Child Is This ?

Traditional

What child is this who, laid to rest
On Mary's lap is sleeping?
Whom Angels greet with anthems sweet,
While shepherds watch are keeping?

(Chorus)
This, this is Christ the King,
Whom shepherds
guard and Angels sing;
Haste, haste, to bring Him laud,
The Babe, the Son of Mary.

Why lies He in such mean estate,
Where ox and ass are feeding?
Good Christians, fear, for sinners here
The silent Word is pleading.

(Chorus)
So bring Him incense, gold and myrrh,
Come peasant, king to own Him;
The King of kings salvation brings,
Let loving hearts enthrone Him.

(Chorus)

# Go Tell It on the Mountain

Traditional

Go tell it on the mountain,
Over the hills and everywhere
Go tell it on the mountain,
That Jesus Christ is born.

While shepherds kept their watching
O'er silent flocks by night,
Behold through out the heavens
There shone a holy light

Go tell it on the mountain
Over the hills and everywhere
Go tell it on the mountain
That Jesus Christ is born

The shepherds feared and trembled,
When lo! above the earth,
Rang out the angels chorus
That hailed our Saviour's birth.

Go tell it on the mountain,
Over the hills and everywhere
Go tell it on the mountain,
That Jesus Christ is born.

Down in a lowly manger
The humble Christ was born
And God sent us salvation
That blessed Christmas morn.

Go tell it on the mountain,
Over the hills and everywhere
Go tell it on the mountain,
That Jesus Christ is born.

Go tell it on the mountain,
Over the hills and everywhere
Go tell it on the mountain,
That Jesus Christ is born.

# Have Yourself a Merry Little Christmas

Have yourself a merry little Christmas
Let your heart be light
From now on our troubles will be out of sight
Have yourself a merry little Christmas
Make the Yuletide gay
From now on, our troubles will be miles away

Here we are as in olden days
Happy golden days of yore
Faithful friends who are dear to us
Gather near to us, once more

Through the years we all will be together
If the fates allow
Hang a shining star upon the highest bow
And have yourself a merry little Christmas now

Have yourself a merry little Christmas
Let your heart be light
From now on our troubles will be out of sight

Have yourself a merry little Christmas
Make the Yuletide gay
From now on our troubles will be miles away

Here we are as in olden days
Happy golden days.of yore
Faithful friends who are dear to us
They gather near to us, once more

Through the years we all will be together
If the fates allow
Hang a shining star upon the highest bow
And have yourself a merry little Christmas now

# Here We Come A Wassailing

Traditional

Here we come a wassailing
Among the leaves so green,
Here we come a wandering
So fair to be seen

Love and joy come to you,
And to you your wassail too,
And God bless you and send you a happy New Year.
And God send you a happy New Year.

We are not daily beggars
Who beg from door to door,
But we are neighbours' children
Whom you have seen before.

Love and joy come to you,
And to you your wassail too,
And God bless you and send you a happy New Year.
And God send you a happy New Year.

God bless the Master of this house,
Likewise the Mistress too;
And all the little children
That round the table go.

Love and joy come to you,
And to you your wassail too,
And God bless you and send you a happy New Year.
And God send you a happy New Year.

# In The Bleak Midwinter

Traditional

In the bleak midwinter, frosty wind made moan,
earth stood hard as iron, water like a stone;
snow had fallen, snow on snow, snow on snow,
in the bleak midwinter, long ago.

Angels and archangels may have gathered there,
cherubim and seraphim thronged the air;
but his mother only, in her maiden bliss,
worshiped the beloved with a kiss.

What can I give him, poor as I am?
If I were a shepherd, I would bring a lamb;
if I were a Wise man, I would do my part;
yet what I can I give him: give him my heart.

# Toy Land

**Traditional**

Toy land, toy land
Li-ittle girl and boy land
While you dwell within it
You are ever happy there

Childhood's joy land
Mi-istic merry toy land
Once you pass its borders
You can ne'er return again

Toy land, toy land
Li-ittle girl and boy land
While you dwell within it
You are ever happy there

Childhood's joy land
Mi-istic merry toy land
Once you pass its borders
You can ne'er return again

Toy land, toy land, toy land, toy land.

# All Through The Night

**Traditional**

Sleep my child and peace attend thee,
All through the night
Guardian angels God will send thee,
All through the night
Soft the drowsy hours are creeping.
Hill and vale in slumber sleeping.
Mother dear her watch his keeping.
All through the night.

# The Twelve Days of Christmas

Traditional

On the first day of Christmas,
my true love gave to me
A partridge in a pear tree.

On the second day of Christmas,
my true love gave to me
Two turtle doves,
And a partridge in a pear tree.

On the third day of Christmas,
my true love gave to me
Three French hens,
Two turtle doves,
And a partridge in a pear tree.

On the fourth day of Christmas,
my true love gave to me
Four calling birds,
Three French hens,
Two turtle doves,
And a partridge in a pear tree.

On the fifth day of Christmas,
my true love gave to me
Five golden rings,
Four calling birds,
Three French hens,
Two turtle doves,
And a partridge in a pear tree.

On the sixth day of Christmas,
my true love gave to me
Six geese a-laying,
Five golden rings,
Four calling birds,
Three French hens,
Two turtle doves,
And a partridge in a pear tree.

On the seventh day of Christmas,
my true love gave to me
Seven swans a-swimming,
Six geese a-laying,
Five golden rings,
Four calling birds,
Three French hens,
Two turtle doves,
And a partridge in a pear tree.

On the eighth day of Christmas,
my true love gave to me
Eight maids a-milking,
Seven swans a-swimming,
Six geese a-laying,
Five golden rings,
Four calling birds,
Three French hens,
Two turtle doves,
And a partridge in a pear tree.

On the ninth day of Christmas,
my true love gave to me
Nine ladies dancing,
Eight maids a-milking,
Seven swans a-swimming,
Six geese a-laying,
Five golden rings,
Four calling birds,
Three French hens,
Two turtle doves,
And a partridge in a pear tree.

On the tenth day of Christmas,
my true love gave to me
Ten lords a-leaping,
Nine ladies dancing,
Eight maids a-milking,
Seven swans a-swimming,
Six geese a-laying,
Five golden rings,
Four calling birds,
Three French hens,
Two turtle doves,
And a partridge in a pear tree.

On the eleventh day of Christmas,
my true love gave to me
Eleven pipers piping,
Ten lords a-leaping,
Nine ladies dancing,
Eight maids a-milking,

Seven swans a-swimming,
Six geese a-laying,
Five golden rings,
Four calling birds,
Three French hens,
Two turtle doves,
And a partridge in a pear tree.

On the twelfth day of Christmas,
my true love gave to me
Twelve drummers drumming,
Eleven pipers piping,
Ten lords a-leaping,
Nine ladies dancing,
Eight maids a-milking,
Seven swans a-swimming,
Six geese a-laying,
Five golden rings,
Four calling birds,
Three French hens,
Two turtle doves,
And a partridge in a pear tree!

47

# O Christmas Tree

Traditional

O Christmas Tree! O Christmas Tree!
Thy candles shine down brightly!

O Christmas Tree! O Christmas Tree!
Much pleasure doth thou bring me;
For every year the Christmas Tree
Brings to us all both joy and glee

O Christmas Tree! O Christmas Tree!
Much pleasure doth thou bring me

49

# O Holy Night

Traditional

O Holy night! The stars are brightly shining
It is the night of the dear Savior's birth
Long lay the world in sin and error pining
'Till He appeared and the soul felt it's worth
A thrill of hope, the weary world rejoices
For yonder breaks a new and glorious morn
Fall on your knees!
O hear the angel voices!
O night divine!
O night, when Christ was born
O night divine, O night, O night divine!

Fall on your knees!
O hear the angel voices!
O night divine!
O night, when Christ was born
O night divine, O night, O night divine!

# Summary

Merry Christmas and Happy New Year!

## Credits

Produced by: **Christopher Norton – Whole World Media, Christopher Pennington**

Musical Arrangements: **Christopher Norton, Christopher Pennington**

Vocal Directors: **Christopher Norton, Christopher Pennington**

Vocals: **Concino Children's Choir, Sara Diamond, Sari Dajani, Wendy Wiseman, Christopher**

Printed and manifactured in China

Copyright © 2010 Distribution CPM inc. & POM Production Oliver Music

No part of this publication may be reproduced, stored in a retrieval system or transmitted in any form or by any means electronic, mechanichal, photocopying, recording or otherwise without the prior written permission of the publisher.